Can you scribble leaves to help Barry hide

Can you scribble Larry Lion's mane?

Can you scribble Shirley Sheep's wool?

Clarence is playing with some wool. Can you scribble it?

Scribble Daddy's new beard.

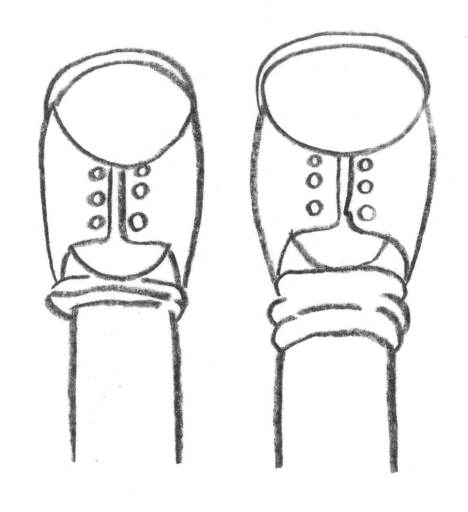

Can you scribble the shoe laces?

The spaghetti is everywhere!
Can you scribble it?

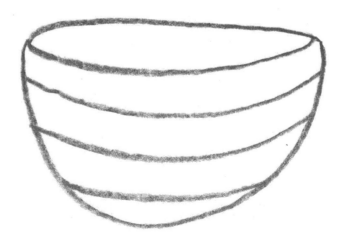

Can you scribble big, shocking hair?

Mummy is having a bath.
Can you scribble the bubbles?

Can you scribble a fence to
stop the naughty horse escaping?

Oh no! William's jumper is unravelling.
Can you scribble the wool?

Can you scribble the rest of Oliver Orangutan's hair?

Can you scribble the flowers,
stalks and leaves?

Can you scribble the spinning clothes?

Scribble a big, bushy tail on Freddy Fox.

There are lots of colourful speeding hula hoops! Can you scribble them?

Scribble a massive, stripey, curly straw to the milkshake.

Can you scribble Croc's big, spiky teeth?

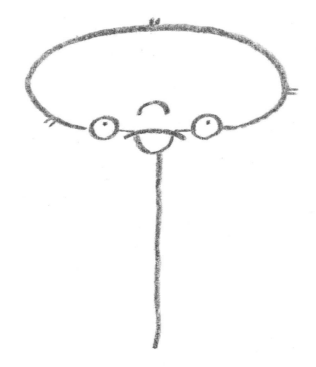

Scribble Sidney Spider's long, hairy legs.

Scribble some big, spiky
leaves for Dorothy
to eat.

Scribble the tiger's colourful stripes.

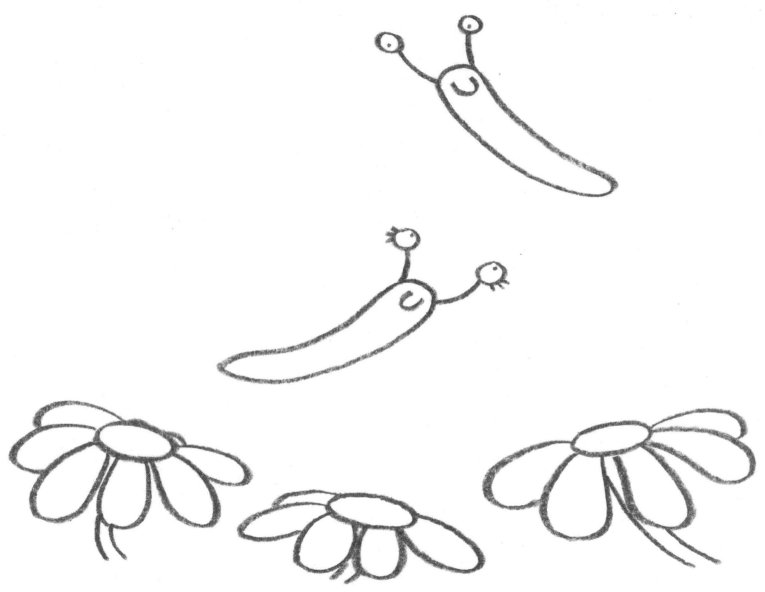

Scribble the butterflies' spotted wings.

Scribble Autumn
leaves in the trees and on the ground.

Scribble the peacock's amazing, swirly tail feathers. They are big and colourful!

Henry Hedgehog has huge, pointy spikes.
Scribble them.

Can you scribble windy sails on the boats?

Scribble the ripples the ducks
have made on the water.

Scribble the pointy wings on the aeroplane and fluffy clouds in the sky.

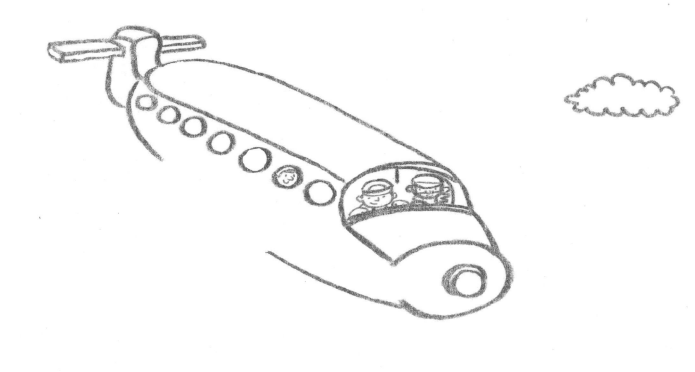

Scribble Chester's
scratchy claw marks.

Scribble a big, soft cushion for Colin.

Scribble Dino's big, red, wobbly jelly!

Blobs? Splats? Stripes? Scribble a pattern.

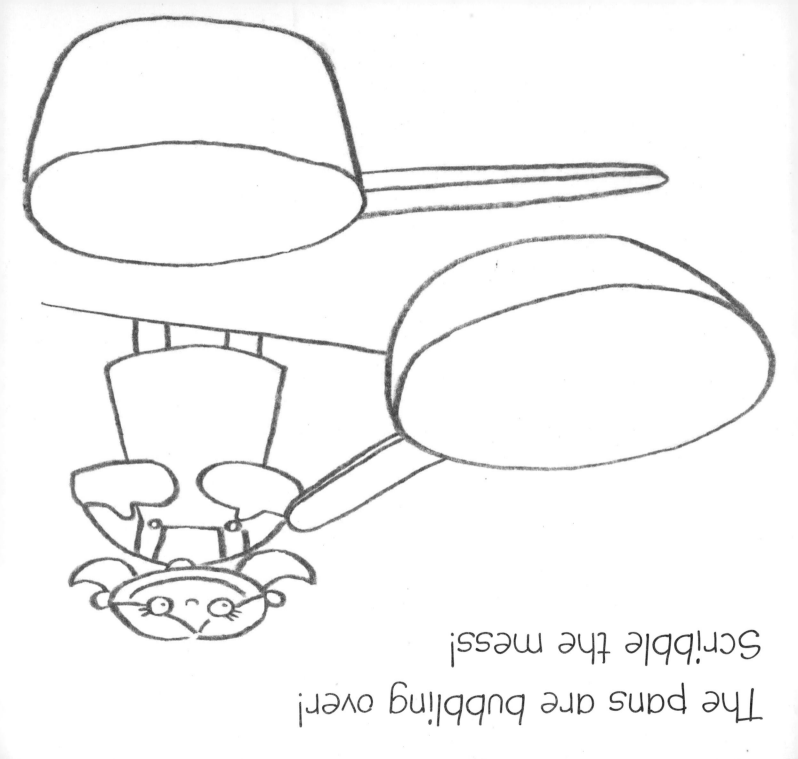

The pans are bubbling over!
Scribble the mess!

Can you scribble
what's on the computer screen?

Eliza has a big, feathered hat. Scribble it!

Scribble a big fire for Fireman Mike to put out. Scribble lots of water and smoke!

Can you scribble some weed

for George to hide in?

Grandpa has long, bushy eyebrows and a big, curly wig. Scribble them!

Harry Hippo has just squashed some colourful flowers. Can you scribble them?

Scribble the bucket of wiggly worms
Jack has collected.

Jolly Jellyfish has long, wiggly tentacles.
Can you scribble them?

Lizzie is going to her ballet class.
Can you scribble her big, fluffy tutu?

Scribble the tangled wool!

Scribble a huge, crashing wave for Surfer Sam.

The cheerleaders have learnt a new dance.
Scribble their huge, colourful pom-poms.

The road is very muddy. Scribble the road and the muddy tyre tracks.

Ben is gargling mouthwash.
Scribble the bubbles.

Scribble the centipede's long, hairy legs!

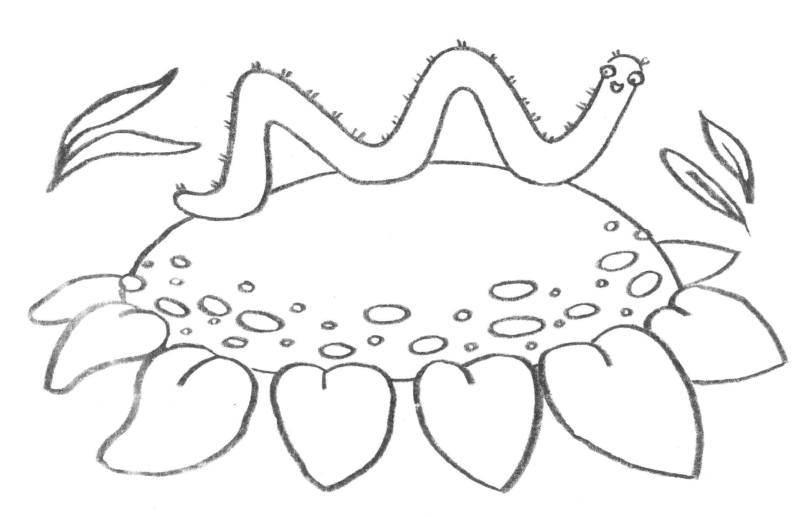

Can you scribble Henrietta's eggs
in her twiggy nest?

Scribble the chameleon's spots
in many colours.

Can you scribble Hilda the highland cow's
fluffy coat?

Scribble Leon's paddles and big splashes.

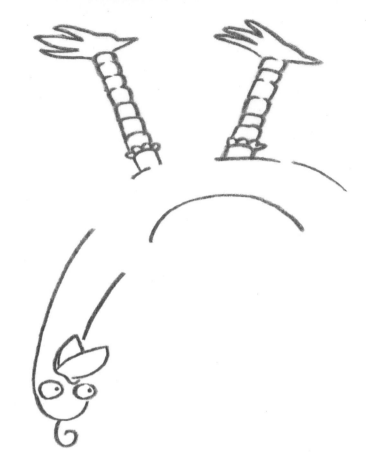

Scribble Olivia's beautiful wings and tail!

Scribble Terry Tortoise's patterned shell.

Can you scribble the baby birds' nest?

Scribble the magical bubbles. Fill the page!

Can you scribble lots of candles on my
birthday cake?

Can you scribble the patterns on my new socks?

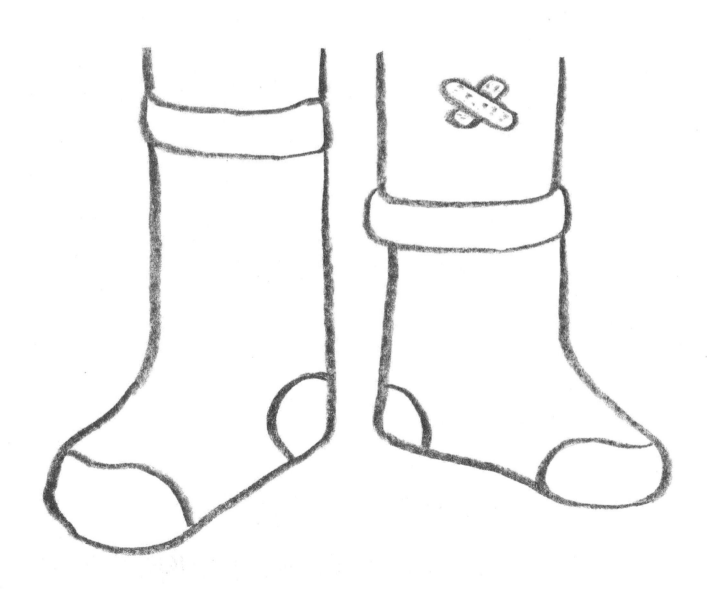

Scribble the spells coming out of
the wizard's book.

It's windy! Scribble more washing blowing on the line.

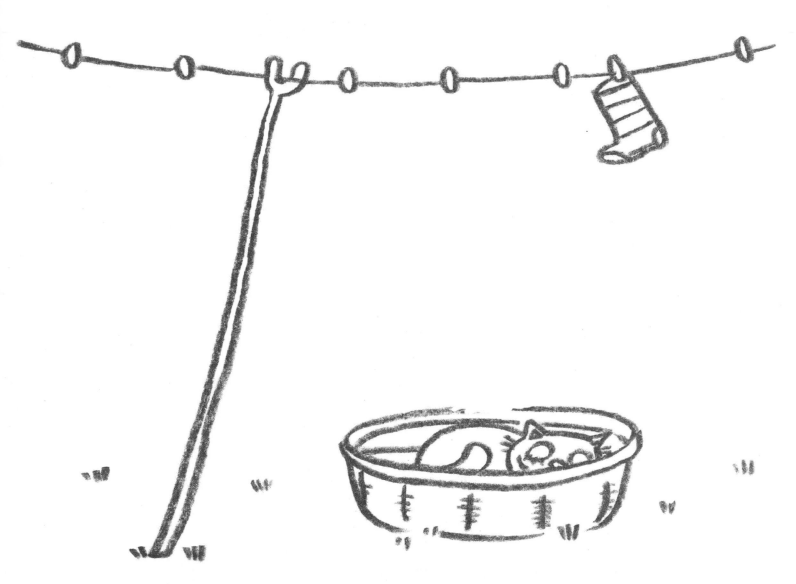

Scribble lots of spots on the ladybird.

Scribble the water splashing from the tap.

Scribble big, muddy wheels on Farmer
Bill's tractor.

Scribble Tony's massive ice-cream.
Don't forget chocolate sauce!

Can you scribble Uncle John's
patterned tie?

Can you scribble what Brian has caught?

Scribble
the butterflies
that Clint
is chasing.

Scribble lots of juggling balls!

Lola's found a rock-pool.
Scribble the creatures.

Scribble the whirlpool of water going down the plughole.

Scribble what Cleo and Clint have
found in the mud.

Cleo is a bridesmaid. Scribble the confetti.

Scribble the wiggly strings and some new balloons.

Poppy has spilt baked beans on the table.
Scribble them.

Scribble big splashes everywhere!

Ziggy is in a spaceship. Scribble the stars!

Scribble the big, orange, red and yellow
flames that Arthur is breathing.

Belinda has bubble gum. Scribble the biggest bubble ever!

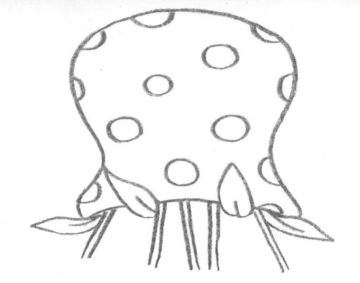

Can you scribble lots of different shaped and colourful flowers?

Can you scribble some big branches for
Bernie to land on?

Scribble the swirl on the snail's shell.
Make it bigger.

Scribble the wheels on the bus until they are solid.

Scribble colourful sweets that fill the jars.

Can you scribble the zebra's stripes?

Can you scribble what computer game is
being played?

The kite is out of control.

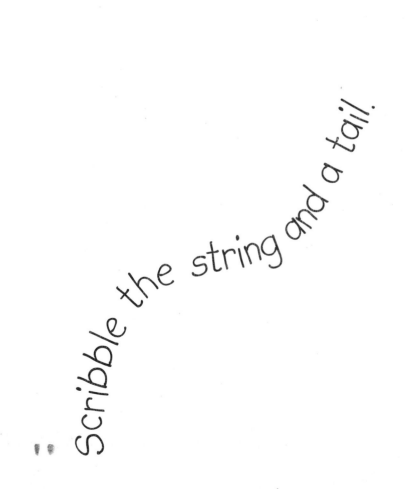

Scribble the string and a tail!

Jim and Bob are playing on the beach.
Can you scribble the sea and sand?

Kate has some big, fluffy, blue candyfloss.
Can you scribble it?

Max has sat on a big, spiky cactus.
Can you scribble it?

Can you scribble the big, wobbly jelly?

Mummy has a patterned top. Scribble some more patterns around Mummy.

Scribble the naughty spider's cobwebs.

Peter Pigeon has lost his feathers.
Can you scribble them?

Scribble Polly's curly hair!

Sally and Josh are splashing in the pool.
Scribble the water.